The Wiggles
PRODUCTION

OCH AYE
THE G'NU

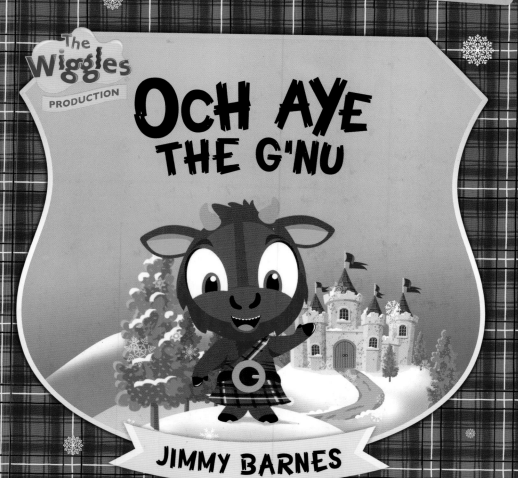

JIMMY BARNES

Though g'nus come from Africa,
he lived in a zoo.
In a land that was wet
and a bitter wind blew.
And the snow and the bagpipes
were all that he knew.
And he went by the name of
young Och Aye the G'Nu.

Now Och Aye the G'Nu
had a voice that cut through.
He was happy and lived
with his friend Kangaroo.
When he danced and he sang
with a hullabaloo.
All the animals cheered
for young Och Aye the G'Nu.

He would tell them to bark,
he would tell them to moo.
As the children rowed by
in a big green canoe.
He would jump in the air
when they came into view.
And the word spread around
about Och Aye the G'Nu.

Well they came from afar,
all the way from Peru.
And they were happy to wait,
they were happy to queue.
All their faces lit up
and the sky seemed so blue.
When they stood and they gazed
at young Och Aye the G'Nu.

Every day there were more,
and the crowds grew and grew.
He would think of new tricks
that he tried to outdo.
Instead of four legs
he could stand up on two.
And the children cheered loudly
YIPPEE!
for Och Aye the G'Nu.

The Queen and the Prince
and the Grand Great Wazoo
came to visit with Sheiks
and a Caliph or two.
They could look but not touch
that was strictly taboo.
They all curtseyed and bowed low
to Och Aye the G'Nu.

He would march up and down
with the Scottish Tattoo.
So they made him a kilt
in a tartan or two.
And the elephant trumpeted
songs that he knew.
An extraordinary beast
was young Och Aye the G'Nu.

They brought hay for the horse,
for the panda bamboo.
For the tigers and lions
they brought Mulligan stew.
Fruit for the bats,
all their wishes came true.
They all ate like kings
'cause of Och Aye the G'Nu.

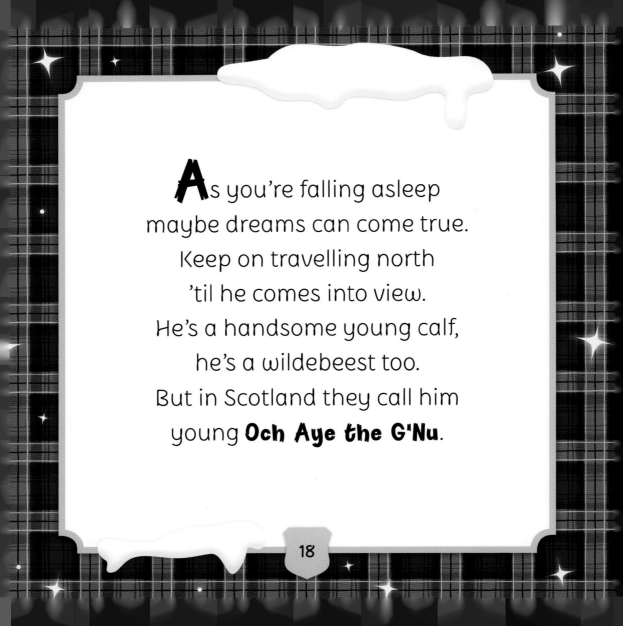

As you're falling asleep
maybe dreams can come true.
Keep on travelling north
'til he comes into view.
He's a handsome young calf,
he's a wildebeest too.
But in Scotland they call him
young **Och Aye the G'Nu**.

THE END